God Is Good

The Egg

and

the Chick

By Mrs. James Swartzentruber

Pictures by Lester Miller

To the Teacher:

This book is designed to give constructive reading practice to pupils using the grade one *Bible Nurture and Reader Series.* It uses words that have been introduced in the reader or can be mastered with phonics skills taught by Unit 2, Lesson 30. A few new words also appear in the story, printed in italics. At the end of the book, these words are listed with pronunciations and / or illustrations to help the children to learn them on their own. Be sure the children understand that the words are vocabulary or sound words except the words in italics, and where to look to learn new words if they need help. They should be able to read this book independently.

Books in this series with their placement according to reading and phonics lessons:

1. The Egg and the Chick   Unit 2, Lesson 30
2. The Squirrel and the Nut   Unit 3, Lesson 5
3. God Makes Seeds That Grow   Unit 3, Lesson 10
4. God Made the Animals   Unit 3, Lesson 15
5. God Made Me   Unit 3, Lesson 20
6. God Made Us   Unit 3, Lesson 25
7. We Should Be Thankful   Unit 3, Lesson 30
8. God Made the Opossum   Unit 4, Lesson 5
9. God Made the Firefly   Unit 4, Lesson 10

Copyright, 1989
By
Rod and Staff Publishers, Inc.
Crockett, Kentucky 41413
Telephone (606) 522-4348
Printed in U.S.A.

ISBN 0-7399-0057-9

Catalog no. 2248

11   12   13   14   —   15   14   13   12   11   10   09

"Jane, it is time to get the eggs," called Mother.

Jane went to get the little pail
she used for the eggs. She liked
this job!

4

There were 13 *chickens*, 12 hens and one . Sometimes Jane would find 10 eggs, or 9, or 11. One time Jane had 12 eggs to give to mother. Every hen gave an egg that day!

Jane gave the *chickens* feed. She gave them water too.

This time Jane had one, two, three, four, five, six, seven, eight, nine, ten eggs in the little pail. There was one more nest to check. A hen sat on that nest.

The hen did not want to get away from the nest. Jane tried to make the hen get away, but the hen tried to peck Jane's hand! Again and again Jane tried to get the hen away from the nest to see if there was an egg in it, but every time the hen tried to peck Jane! Jane was not happy!

"Mother," said Jane, "I have 10 eggs. But I could not see if one nest had an egg. A hen sat on it, and she would not let me see if there was an egg! Every time I tried to get the hen away, she tried to peck me! She did not want to let me get it!"

Mother smiled. "That is *nice*."

"What do you mean, Mother?" asked Jane.

Jane did not think it was *nice* that the hen tried to peck! Why did Mother say that?

9

"I did not mean that it was *nice* that she tried to peck you," said Mother. "But it is *nice* that she wants to sit on the eggs in the nest.

"That is God's plan for the hen. She sits and sits on the eggs for many days. Then the eggs crack open, and out come little *baby* chicks!

"Just leave the eggs in the nest if the hen sits on them. Do not get them."

Jane smiled. She would like little *baby* chicks! She would be happy to let the hen sit on the nest now!

The hen sat on the nest many days. Every day Jane gave the *chickens* feed. Every day she gave the *chickens* water. Every day Jane had eggs in the little pail to give to Mother. Every day she let the hen sit on the nest. She sat and sat and sat.

Sometimes the hen would eat some feed and drink some water. But she did not stay away from the nest very long. She sat and sat and sat.

One day when Jane went out
with the little pail to get the eggs,
there was a little "Peep, peep,
peep, peep." There *beside* the
hen, Jane could see a little, yellow
baby chick!

14

Jane ran to the house. "Mother! Mother! The hen has a little *baby* chick! Come and see it!"

Mother went with Jane. They could see one, two little, yellow *baby* chicks! "Peep, peep, peep, peep."

Mother Hen still sat on the nest. There were more eggs in the nest.

Then one day Mother Hen
was not on the nest at all. She
had 10 yellow, *baby* chicks!

Jane liked to play with the little chicks. She liked the little peeps they made, "Peep, peep, peep."

"I am glad God made little chicks," Jane told Mother.

"Yes," Mother said with a smile. "The Bible says, 'And God saw every thing that he had made, and . . .' "

" '. . . Behold, it was very good,' " finished Jane.

chickens (chik • enz)

nice (nīs)

baby (bā • bē)

beside (be + side)